WHAT'S NEW SCOOBY-DOO? ™

Illustrated by Art Mawhinney

Written by Jamie Elder

Published by
Louis Weber, C.E.O.
Publications International, Ltd.
7373 North Cicero Avenue
Lincolnwood, Illinois 60712

www.pilbooks.com

Look and Find is a registered trademark of
Publications International, Ltd.

Manufactured in China.

8 7 6 5 4 3 2 1

ISBN 0-7853-9007-3

Publications International, Ltd.

Scooby-Doo, Shaggy, Fred, Daphne, and Velma are at the Space Center when an alien egg grows and hatches! With an alien on the loose, the gang finds that everything is not what it is cracked up to be. Look for Scooby and Shaggy's space snacks to help solve the mystery.

Loaf of bread

Cherry pie

Turkey

Watermelon

T-bone steak

Spiral ham

Chocolate cake

The gang is in New Orleans for Mardi Gras, so it is guaranteed that they will see a ghost. Sure enough in the water park next to the cemetery, two Civil War ghosts, Jed and Caleb Leland, chase after them. Find Scooby-Doo, Shaggy, Fred, Daphne, and Velma and help them escape the Leland Brothers.

Scooby-Doo

Velma

Fred

Shaggy

Daphne

Caleb Leland

Jed Leland

The gang finds out that the Mystery Machine once belonged to the Mystery Kids band! When the van starts acting weird, they take it to their mechanic, Murph. At the shop, they find out that Murph has been acting weird, too. In Murph's private office, there is a Mystery Kids shrine. Look for these Mystery Kids things to help solve the mystery.

Mystery Kids lunch box

Mystery Kids night-light

Mystery Kids record album

Mystery Kids alarm clock

Mystery Kids T-shirt

Mystery Kids lamp

Mystery Kids board game

The gang goes to Las Vegas to catch a concert, but the ghost of Rufus Raucous is trying to sabotage it. But wait! The real Rufus Raucous is alive and well and sabotages the ghost with his famous tricks. Look for these magical things.

Pack of cards

Top hat

Floating bottle

Magic scarf

Dove box

Linking rings

Sword box

Scooby! Scooby-Doo, where are you? All the animals in the jungle have gone ape. They are wild and glowing, and Scooby is among them. Help solve the mystery by looking for these animals in their altered states.

Scooby

Jocko

Lion

Leopard

Gorilla

Zebra

Rhinoceros

While shopping for a gift, Scooby, Shaggy, Fred, Daphne, and Velma find that the toys aren't playing around when they come to life in the toy store. Stay with the gang after the mall closes and help them uncover the real mystery by finding these subversive toys.

Battleship

G.I. Steve

Paratrooper

Jeep

Soldier

Tank

Bomber

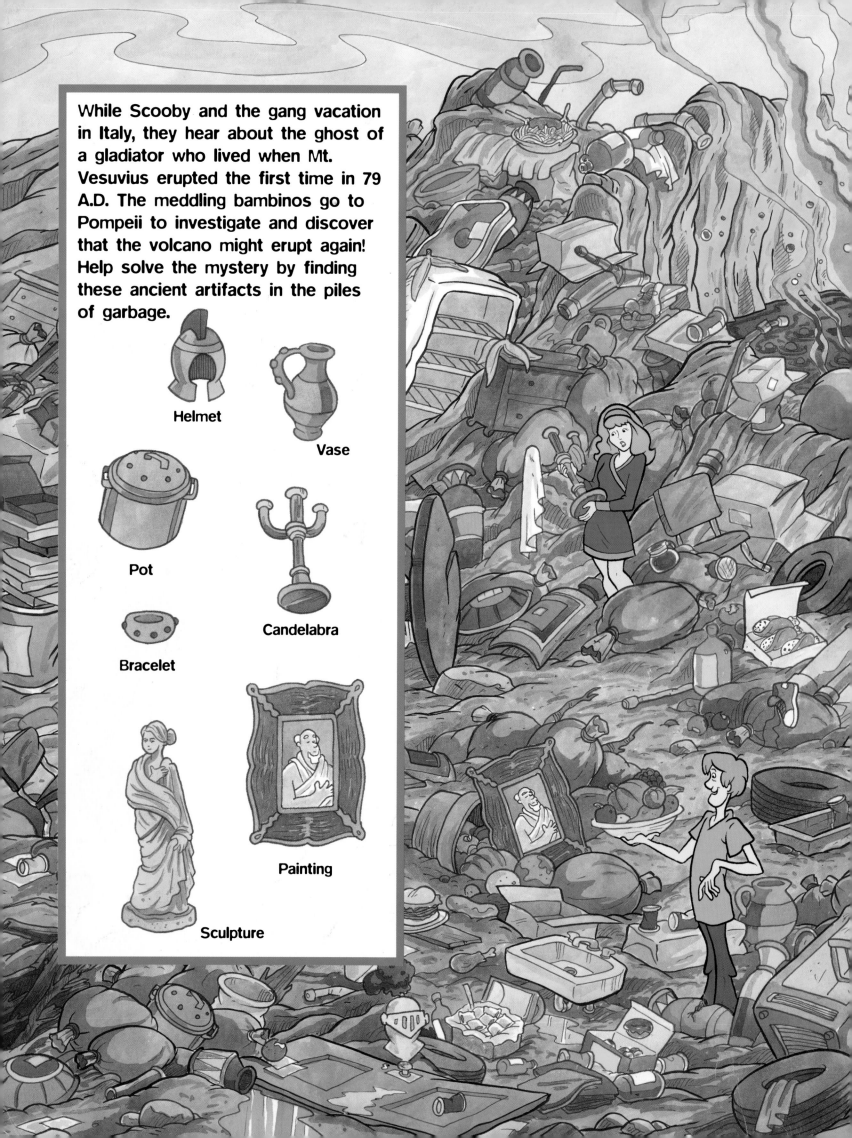

While Scooby and the gang vacation in Italy, they hear about the ghost of a gladiator who lived when Mt. Vesuvius erupted the first time in 79 A.D. The meddling bambinos go to Pompeii to investigate and discover that the volcano might erupt again! Help solve the mystery by finding these ancient artifacts in the piles of garbage.

Helmet

Vase

Pot

Candelabra

Bracelet

Painting

Sculpture

Go back to the tank room at the Space Center and look for the janitor's undercover cleaning supplies.

_____ Eavesdrop mop

_____ Zoom broom

_____ Giveaway spray

_____ Tracks wax

_____ Hush brush

_____ Microscope soap

Go back and help Daphne find her spare shoes that were scattered in the chase.

_____ True shoe

_____ Blue shoe

_____ Moo shoe

_____ Glue shoe

_____ Flew shoe

_____ Cuckoo shoe

Go back to Murph's private office and look for evidence of his other hobbies.

_____ Coin collection

_____ Stamp collection

_____ Origami

_____ Needlepoint

_____ Accordion

_____ Golf clubs

Go back to Las Vegas and help Rufus and the gang understand the gravity of the situation by finding these clues.

_____ Scooby's collar

_____ Fred's keys

_____ Shaggy's belt buckle

_____ Daphne's compact

_____ Velma's watch

Go back to the jungle and find all the animal crackers that Shaggy has spilled.

_____ Lion

_____ Giraffe

_____ Turtle

_____ Bear

_____ Elephant

_____ Camel

Go back to the mall and find the evidence that the toys are trying to keep secret.

_____ A crack

_____ A drill

_____ A jackhammer

_____ A pile of stones

_____ A coil of rope

_____ A bag of cement

Go back to the volcano and find leftover Italian food that Scooby and Shaggy cannot resist.

_____ Spaghetti

_____ Linguini

_____ Lasagna

_____ Ravioli

_____ Pizza

_____ Cannoli

Go back to the baseball park, where flaming fastballs are flying, and find these other hot things.

_____ Hot dog

_____ Hot sauce

_____ Jalapeño peppers

_____ Cinnamon candy

_____ Hot chocolate

_____ Spicy meatball sandwich